My Spelling Workbook

Book A

This book belongs to:

....

Includes CD
'Interactive Spelling Activities'

Prim-Ed
Publishing

www.prim-ed.com

My Spelling Workbook *(Book A)*

Published by Prim-Ed Publishing 2011
2nd edition 2011
Copyright© Prim-Ed Publishing 2011
ISBN 978-1-84654-189-6
PR–2280

Titles available in this series:
My Spelling Workbook *(Book A)*
My Spelling Workbook *(Book B)*
My Spelling Workbook *(Book C)*
My Spelling Workbook *(Book D)*
My Spelling Workbook *(Book E)*
My Spelling Workbook *(Book F)*
My Spelling Workbook *(Book G)*

Offices in:
UK and Republic of Ireland:
Bosheen
New Ross
County Wexford
www.prim-ed.com

Australia:
PO Box 332
Greenwood
Western Australia 6924
www.ricpublications.com.au

Welcome to **My Spelling Workbook and CD**.

This book and CD have lots of activities to help you learn to spell.

You should follow this method when you are learning to spell each word.

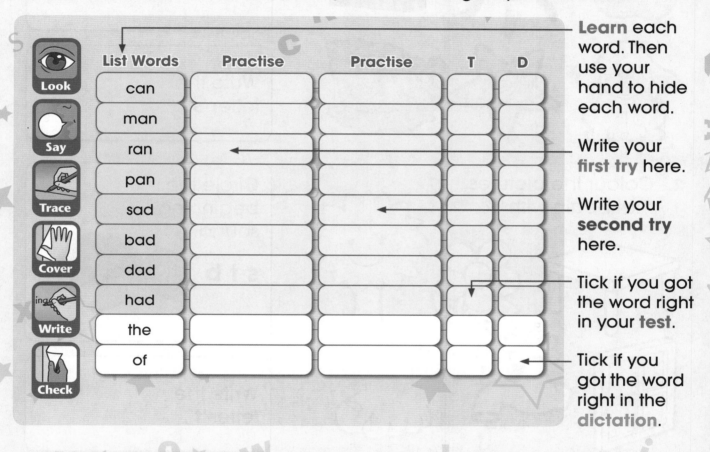

Learn each word. Then use your hand to hide each word.

Write your **first try** here.

Write your **second try** here.

Tick if you got the word right in your **test**.

Tick if you got the word right in the **dictation**.

Contents

Beginning Sounds

1. Circle the pictures that begin with 's'.

Circle the beginning sound.

s t b

Write the letter 's'.

2. Colour the pictures that begin with 't'.

Circle the beginning sound.

s t b

Write the letter 't'.

3. Circle the pictures that begin with 'b'.

quack

Circle the beginning sound.

s t b

Write the letter 'b'.

My Spelling Workbook A—Prim-Ed Publishing—www.prim-ed.com

4. Circle the pictures that begin with '**c**'.

Circle the beginning sound.

c f r

Write the letter '**c**'.

5. Colour the pictures that begin with '**f**'.

Circle the beginning sound.

c f r

Write the letter '**f**'.

6. Circle the pictures that begin with '**r**'.

Circle the beginning sound.

c f r

Write the letter '**r**'.

Beginning Sounds

1. Circle the pictures that begin with 'e'.

Circle the beginning sound.

e g h

Write the letter 'e'.

2. Colour the pictures that begin with 'g'.

Circle the beginning sound.

e g h

Write the letter 'g'.

3. Circle the pictures that begin with 'h'.

Circle the beginning sound.

e g h

Write the letter 'h'.

My Spelling Workbook A—Prim-Ed Publishing—www.prim-ed.com

4. Circle the pictures that begin with 'o'.

Circle the beginning sound.

o m n

Write the letter 'o'.

5. Colour the pictures that begin with 'm'.

Circle the beginning sound.

o m n

Write the letter 'm'.

6. Circle the pictures that begin with 'n'.

Circle the beginning sound.

o m n

Write the letter 'n'.

Beginning Sounds

1. Circle the pictures that begin with '**a**'.

Circle the beginning sound.

a l w

Write the letter '**a**'.

2. Colour the pictures that begin with '**l**'.

Circle the beginning sound.

a l w

Write the letter '**l**'.

3. Circle the pictures that begin with '**w**'.

Circle the beginning sound.

a l w

Write the letter '**w**'.

My Spelling Workbook A—Prim-Ed Publishing—www.prim-ed.com

4. Circle the pictures that begin with '**i**'.

Circle the beginning sound.

i k p

Write the letter '**i**'.

5. Colour the pictures that begin with '**k**'.

Circle the beginning sound. **i k p**

Write the letter '**k**'.

6. Circle the pictures that begin with '**p**'.

Circle the beginning sound.

i k p

Write the letter '**p**'.

Beginning Sounds

1. Circle the pictures that begin with '**d**'.

Circle the beginning sound.

d q u

Write the letter '**d**'.

2. Colour the pictures that begin with '**q**'.

Circle the beginning sound.

d q u

Write the letter '**q**'.

3. Circle the pictures that begin with '**u**'.

Circle the beginning sound.

d q u

Write the letter '**u**'.

My Spelling Workbook A—Prim-Ed Publishing—www.prim-ed.com

4. Colour the pictures that begin with '**j**'.

Circle the beginning sound.

j   v

Write the letter '**j**'.

5. Circle the pictures that begin with '**v**'.

Circle the beginning sound.

j   v

Write the letter '**v**'.

Beginning Sounds

1. Circle the picture that begins with '**x**'.

Circle the beginning sound.

x y z

Write the letter '**x**'.

2. Colour the pictures that begin with '**y**'.

Circle the beginning sound.

x y z

Write the letter '**y**'.

3. Circle the pictures that begin with '**z**'.

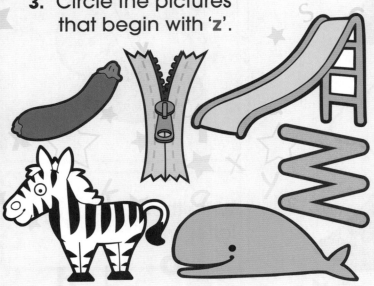

Circle the beginning sound.

x y z

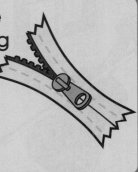

Write the letter '**z**'.

My Spelling Workbook A—Prim-Ed Publishing—www.prim-ed.com

Circle the beginning sound.

b d

f v

j g

m n

d t

i e

a u

b d

f v

j g

m n

d t

i e

a u

p t

Beginning Sounds

Write the beginning sound.

p o s x c d w a g t m b n f v

___og

___et

___ed

___un

___at

___ate

___-ray

___ap

___nt

___ctopus

___ig

___ish

___eb

___at

___ase

My Spelling Workbook A—Prim-Ed Publishing—www.prim-ed.com

Write the beginning sound.

___et

___ip

___at

___oyo

___gg

___op

___est

___ox

___ug

___og

___ey

___nsect

___rum

___uack

___mbrella

e h l u i d q y j k n r z b m

Final Sounds

Circle the end sound.

b g **t**

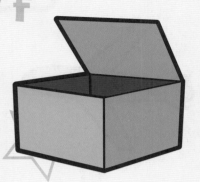

d f **m**

b g t
n p k

x t s

l b m

g m **d**

l n **t**

f **p** g

m **n** k

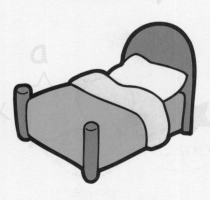

b **d** l

n d p

My Spelling Workbook A—Prim-Ed Publishing—www.prim-ed.com

Circle the end sound.

z t p

p g k

t m n

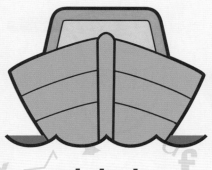

t l d

d s l

n m b

s x t

p d b

f b l

t d n

p d t

b s z

Write the end sound.

b
m
k
t
g
d
n
p

ca___

ste___

bi___

mo___

fro___

ne___

hoo___

li___

pi___

cu___

moo___

for___

Write the end sound.

bu___

bi___

si___

6

bir___

ba___

10

te___

ten___

foa___

ro___

lea___

fo___

we___

s
f
d
x
t
n
b
l

Medial Sounds

1. (a) Circle the pictures with an 'a' sound in the middle.

(b) Circle the pictures with an 'i' sound in the middle.

2. Write 'a' or 'i' in the middle of each word.

p__g   b__t   f__n

b__n   f__n   m__p

1. (a) Circle the pictures with an 'e' sound in the middle.

(b) Circle the pictures with an 'o' sound in the middle.

2. Write 'e' or 'o' in the middle of each word.

j__t   h__n   d__g

p__t   b__d   m__p

Medial Sounds

1. (a) Circle the pictures with an 'a' sound in the middle.

(b) Circle the pictures with an 'u' sound in the middle.

2. Write 'a' or 'u' in the middle of each word.

c__p   b__s   b__t

m__g   r__t   b__g

1. (a) Circle the pictures with an 'e' sound in the middle.

(b) Circle the pictures with an 'i' sound in the middle.

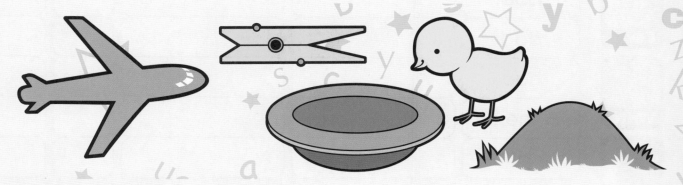

2. Write 'e' or 'i' in the middle of each word.

l__g   p__n   t__n

p__t   z__p   b__b

Unit 1

Look

Say

Trace

Cover

Write

Check

List Words	Practise	Practise	T	D
can				
man				
ran				
pan				
sad				
bad				
dad				
had				
the				
of				

Fill the Gaps

1. (a) can

   ca____

   c____ ____

   ____ ____ ____

   (b) pan

   pa____

   p____ ____

   (c) dad

   da____

   d____ ____ ____

   ____ ____ ____

Word Worm

2. Circle each word you can find in the word worm.

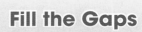

cansaddadrantheman

My Spelling Workbook A—Prim-Ed Publishing—www.prim-ed.com

| an | ad |

Spelling Sums

3. (a) c + an = _can_

    (b) r + an = _____

    (c) s + ad = _____

    (d) b + ad = _____

    (e) p + an = _____

Shape Sorter

5. Guess the word by its shape.

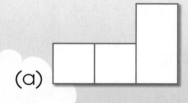
(a)

(b)

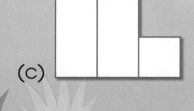
(c)

(d)

Read and Draw

4. A sad man.

Spelling Patterns

6. Use the correct colour for these words.

    (a) Colour the 'an' words red.

    (b) Colour the 'ad' words blue.

man	sad
pan	can
dad	had

Unit 2

Look

Say

Trace

Cover

Write

Check

List Words	Practise	Practise	T	D
pet				
met				
set				
wet				
am				
ham				
jam				
ram				
to				
by				

Fill the Gaps

1. (a) met   (b) pet   (c) ham

    me___   pe___   ha___

    m___ ___   p___ ___   h___ ___

    ___ ___ ___   ___ ___ ___   ___ ___ ___

Word Worm

2. Circle each word you can find in the word worm.

towetjambypetram

et | am

Spelling Sums

3. (a) r + am = ___ram___

(b) w + et = _____

(c) j + am = _____

(d) h + am = _____

(e) m + et = _____

Shape Sorter

5. Guess the word by its shape.

(a)

(b)

(c)

(d)

Read and Draw

4. A jar of jam.

Spelling Patterns

6. Use the correct colour for these words.

(a) Colour the 'et' words red.

(b) Colour the 'am' words blue.

  met jam ram

 set pet

 ham

Look

Say

Trace

Cover

Write

Check

List Words	Practise	Practise	T	D
bells				
red				
star				
fun				
cake				
Santa				
tag				
tree				
did				
got				

Find the Word

1. Write each word on the grid.

(a)

(b)

(c) You have it at the circus.

(d)

(e)

Word Worm

2. Circle each word you can find in the word worm.

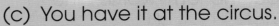
redtagfuncakegotSanta

Christmas

Read and Draw

3. A Christmas tree.

Word Search

4. Find these words in the word search.

bells	Santa
red	tag
star	tree
fun	did
cake	
got	

s
t a g
f u n o p
t a t t r
r c a k e
e r s c d
e e t d e s
e a i
l d r d k
b e l l s

Shape Sorter

5. Guess the word by its shape.

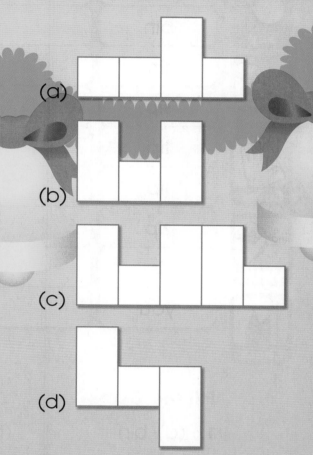

(a)

(b)

(c)

(d)

Rhyming Words

6. Write a Christmas word that rhymes with these words.

(a) bed _____

(b) bee _____

(c) sun _____

(d) car _____

(e) rag _____

(f) sells _____

List Words	Practise	Practise	T	D
win				
fin				
bin				
tin				
sip				
tip				
lip				
zip				
is				
you				

Look

Say

Trace

Cover

Write

Check

Fill the Gaps

1. (a) bin   (b) sip   (c) win

    bi___   si___   wi___

    b___ ___   s___ ___   w___ ___

    ___ ___ ___   ___ ___ ___   ___ ___ ___

Spelling Patterns

2. Use the correct colour for these words.

(a) Colour the 'in' words red.

(b) Colour the 'ip' words blue.

sip

zip

tip

win

fin

tin

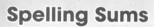 **in** **ip**

Spelling Sums

3. (a) f + in = _fin_

(b) b + in = _____

(c) s + ip = _____

(d) z + ip = _____

(e) w + in = _____

Read and Draw

4. A tin of soup.

All Mixed Up

5. Unjumble these words.

(a) pzi _____

(b) uoy _____

(c) nti _____

(d) lpi _____

Word Worm

6. Circle each word you can find in the word worm.

tintipbinissipyouzip

ot | it

Look

Say

Trace

Cover

Write

Check

List Words	Practise	Practise	T	D
cot				
hot				
dot				
pot				
bit				
pit				
sit				
it				
that				
if				

Fill the Gaps

1. (a) dot   (b) pit   (c) cot

   do___   pi___   co___

   d_____   p_____   c_____

   _____   _____   _____

Word Worm

2. Circle each word you can find in the word worm.

ifhotpotthatbitdot

All Mixed Up

3. Unjumble these words.

   (a) fi _____

   (b) tsi _____

   (c) pto _____

   (d) ttha _____

Read and Draw

4. A hot sun.

Spelling Sums

5. (a) h + ot = ___hot___

   (b) b + it = _____

   (c) p + ot = _____

   (d) c + ot = _____

   (e) s + it = _____

Spelling Patterns

6. Use the correct colour for these words.

   (a) Colour the 'ot' words green.

   (b) Colour the 'it' words red.

sit   hot

cot   bit

pit   dot

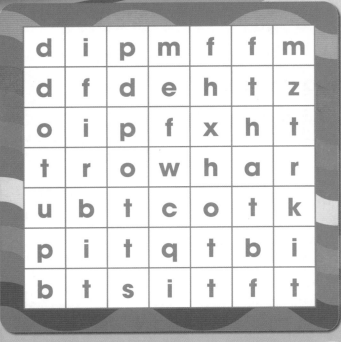

Word Search

7. Find these list words in the word search.

hot

it

if

that

pot

dot

pit

sit

bit

cot

Missing Letters

8. Write '**ot**' or '**it**' to make a word.

(a) b_____ (b) s_____

(c) c_____ (d) d_____

Missing Words

9. Complete the sentences using these words.

hot   **If**   **bit**

(a) It was so _____ today we went for a swim.

(b) Can I have a _____ of cake, please?

(c) _____ you go too fast, you will crash.

List Words

cot
hot
dot
pot
bit
pit
sit
it
that
if

ot it

Word Maker

10. How many words can you make?

_____   _____

_____   cot   _____

s a
d h c p
w **ot** t

What am I?

11. I am tiny.

I am round.

I am black.

I am a _____.

Draw Me

Match Me

12. Circle the word in the box that matches the given word.

(a) that

| tat | that | tath | taht |

(b) pit

| pet | tip | pit | pot |

(c) dot

| dut | tod | top | dot |

Unit 6

List Words	Practise	Practise	T	D
hug				
rug				
bug				
mug				
jug				
bag				
rag				
wag				
put				
was				

Look
Say
Trace
Cover
Write
Check

Fill the Gaps

1. (a) rug   (b) bag   (c) put

   ru____   ba____   pu____

   r_____   b_____   p_____

Spelling Patterns

2. Use the correct colour for these words.

   (a) Colour the 'ag' words dark green.

   (b) Colour the 'ug' words red.

rug   bug   rag   mug   wag   hug

34   My Spelling Workbook A—Prim-Ed Publishing—www.prim-ed.com

Spelling Sums

3. (a) j + ug = _____ *jug*

    (b) b + ag = _____

    (c) m + ug = _____

    (d) b + ug = _____

    (e) w + ag = _____

Read and Draw

4. A jug of water.

All Mixed Up

5. Unjumble these words.

    (a) wga _____

    (b) tup _____

    (c) swa _____

    (d) gru _____

Word Worm

6. Circle each word you can find in the word worm.

hugbugwasputrugrag

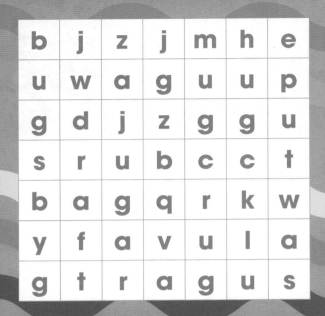

b	j	z	j	m	h	e
u	w	a	g	u	u	p
g	d	j	z	g	g	u
s	r	u	b	c	c	t
b	a	g	q	r	k	w
y	f	a	v	u	l	a
g	t	r	a	g	u	s

Word Search

7. Find these words in the word search.

hug   bag

bug   rag

rug   wag

mug   put

jug   was

More than One

8. Add '**s**' to make more than one.

(a) mug _____ (b) bag _____

(c) hug _____ (d) bug _____

Spelling Words

9. (a) Take the 'p' off '**put**' and put in 'c'.

(b) Take the 'u' off '**bug**' and put in 'i'.

(c) Take the 'w' off '**was**' and put in 'h'.

(d) Take the 'j' off '**jug**' and put in 't'.

List Words

hug

rug

bug

mug

jug

bag

rag

wag

put

was

ug **ag**

Find Me

10. Circle the correct word.

(a) hug

    jug

    bug

(b) rug

    mug

    hug

(c) hug

    mug

    jug

(d) rag

    wag

    bag

(e) wag

    rag

    bag

Missing Letters

11. Write the missing letters.

(a) p___t

(b) m_____

(c) j_____

(d) w___s

(e) h_____

Word Hunt

12. (a) Which words start with 'w'? _____

    (b) Which word is often given by Mum or Dad? _____

    (c) Which word is an insect? _____

Unit (7)

Look

Say

Trace

Cover

Write

Check

List Words	Practise	Practise	T	D
mix				
six				
box				
fox				
cut				
hut				
but				
nut				
are				
as				

Fill the Gaps

1. (a) fox   (b) six   (c) nut

     fo____   si____   nu____

     f____ ____   s____ ____   n____ ____

     ____ ____ ____   ____ ____ ____   ____ ____ ____

Spelling Patterns

2. Use the correct colour for these words.

(a) Colour the 'ix' and 'ox' words green.

(b) Colour the 'ut' words red.

but **mix**

cut **hut**

fox **nut**

My Spelling Workbook A—Prim-Ed Publishing—www.prim-ed.com

Spelling Sums

3. (a) m + ix = _mix_

(b) f + ox = _____

(c) h + ut = _____

(d) s + ix = _____

(e) c + ut = _____

All Mixed Up

5. Unjumble these words.

(a) tun _____

(b) sa _____

(c) rea _____

(d) xbo _____

Read and Draw

4. A garden hut.

Word Worm

6. Circle each word you can find in the word worm.

cutsixaremixbox

Unit ⑦

ix · ox · ut

n	b	b	s	q	f	y
a	s	o	i	r	k	n
f	o	x	x	t	g	u
h	u	t	t	b	u	t
m	i	x	b	z	a	h
g	o	i	h	l	r	r
c	u	t	g	y	e	r

Word Search

7. Find these words in the word search.

mix	hut
six	but
box	nut
fox	are
cut	as

What Am I?

8. I am hard and small.

You can eat me.

I am part of a fruit.

I am a _____.

Missing Words

9. Complete the sentences using these words.

six   as   are   as   fox

(a) He is _____ fast _____ the wind.

(b) An ant has _____ legs.

(c) A _____ has a big tail.

(d) We _____ going to school.

List Words

mix
six
box
fox
cut
hut
but
nut
are
as

Find Me

10. Circle the correct word.

(a) nut

hut

but

(b) cut

hut

but

(c) six

box

fox

(d) fox

six

box

Match Me

11. Circle the word in the box that matches the given word.

(a) are

| arr | are | ar |

(b) but

| but | bat | bet |

(c) cut

| cat | cute | cut |

Secret Words

12. (a) Take the 'e' off '**are**' and put in 't'. _____

(b) Take the 's' off '**as**' and put in 't'. _____

(c) Take the 'u' off '**nut**' and put in 'o'. _____

(d) Take the 'u' off '**but**' and put in 'a'. _____

Look

Say

Trace

Cover

Write

Check

List Words	Practise	Practise	T	D
we				
me				
he				
she				
be				
bed				
wed				
fed				
with				
his				

Fill the Gaps

1. (a) bed   (b) she   (c) wed

    be___   sh___   we___

    b___ ___   s___ ___   w___ ___

    ___ ___ ___   ___ ___ ___   ___ ___ ___

Spelling Patterns

2. Use the correct colour for these words.

    (a) Colour the words ending in '**e**' orange.

    (b) Colour the '**ed**' words green.

fed   wed   he   me   we   bed

Spelling Sums

3. (a) b + ed = _bed_

 (b) wi + th = _____

 (c) f + ed = _____

 (d) w + ed = _____

 (e) sh + e = _____

Read and Draw

4. A boy with his teddy.

Word Worm

5. Circle each word you can find in the word worm.

bewithhisbedwefed

Word Maker

6. How many words can you make?

_____

_____

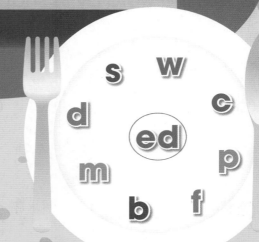

What Am I?

3. I am small but I can grow tall.

You can plant me.

I am a _____ .

Shape Sorter

4. Guess the word by its shape.

(a)

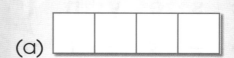

(b)

(c)

(d)

Small Words

5. Write the small words in these big words.

(a) been _____*be*_____

_____*bee*_____

(b) meet _____

(c) weed _____

Spelling Patterns

6. Use the correct colour for these words.

(a) Colour the 'eed' words red.

(b) Colour the 'een' words yellow.

feed

been

weed

seed

seen

need

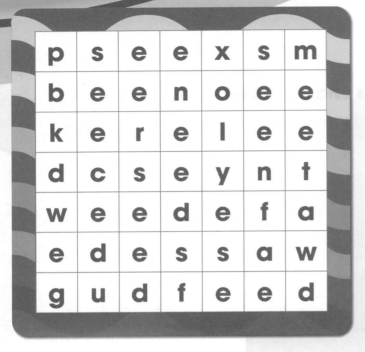

Word Search

7. Find these words in the word search.

see	need
been	feed
weed	seen
seed	yes
meet	saw

Word Maker

8. How many words can you make?

_____ _____

_____ _____

s f

n w

Missing Words

9. Complete the sentences using these words.

    saw

(a) We all _____ the film.

(b) We will _____ Mum at the shops.

(c) I want to _____ that new film.

(d) We went to _____ bread to the swans.

(e) I have never _____ in her house.

My Spelling Workbook A—Prim-Ed Publishing—www.prim-ed.com

Draw and Label

10. Draw and label

(a) a weed

(b) a seed

All Mixed Up

11. Unjumble these words.

(a) nese _____ (b) wsa _____

(c) teem _____ (d) sey _____

Match Me

12. Circle each word in the bug that matches the given word.

(a) see   cee   sea   see

(b) meet   mete   meet   meat

(c) seed   sead   ceed   seed

List Words
see
been
weed
seed
meet
need
feed
seen
yes
saw

Unit 13

Look

Say

Trace

Cover

Write

Check

List Words	Practise	Practise	T	D
moon				
room				
hood				
zoo				
all				
call				
ball				
small				
this				
have				

Fill the Gaps

1. (a) room

    roo___

    ro___ ___

    r___ ___ ___

    ___ ___ ___ ___

    (b) hood

    hoo___

    ho___ ___

    h___ ___ ___

    ___ ___ ___ ___

    (c) ball

    bal___

    ba___ ___

    b___ ___ ___

    ___ ___ ___ ___

More Than One

2. Add '**s**' to make more than one.

    (a) ball _____

    (b) room _____

    (c) moon _____

    (d) zoo _____

Spelling Sums

3. (a) m + oon = _moon_

   (b) c + all = _____

   (c) sm + all = _____

   (d) r + oom = _____

   (e) th + is = _____

All Mixed Up

4. Unjumble these words.

   (a) ozo _____

   (b) oorm _____

   (c) aveh _____

   (d) lsalm _____

Shape Sorter

5. Guess the word by its shape.

(a)

(b)

(c)

(d)

Word Worm

6. Circle each word you can find in the word worm.

smallzoohavethisallball

s	m	a	l	l	b	f
r	o	o	m	a	a	n
c	o	y	z	h	l	t
a	n	a	p	o	l	h
l	z	l	a	o	o	i
l	o	l	a	d	r	s
v	o	r	h	a	v	e

Word Search

7. Find these words in the word search.

moon   call

room   ball

hood   small

zoo   this

all   have

What Am I?

8. I keep your head dry.

I am often on a coat.

I am a _____.

Missing Words

9. Complete the sentences using these words.

have   ball   zoo   small

(a) I saw a giraffe at the _____.

(b) The _____ rolled down the road.

(c) Ants are very _____.

(d) I _____ a dog called Spot.

List Words

moon

room

hood

zoo

all

call

ball

small

this

have

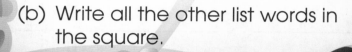

oo   **all**

Spelling Patterns

10. (a) Write the 'all' words on the ball.

(b) Write all the other list words in the square.

Missing Letters

11. Write '**oo**' or '**all**' to make a word.

(a) r_____m   (b) sm_____   (c) h_____d

(d) z_____   (e) c_____   (f) m_____n

Secret Words

12. (a) Take the 'm' off '**moon**' and put in 's'. _____

(b) Take the 'c' off '**call**' and put in 't'. _____

(c) Take the 'h' off '**hood**' and put in 'g'. _____

(d) Take the 's' off '**this**' and put in 'n'. _____

Unit 14

	List Words	Practise	Practise	T	D
Look	and				
Say	sand				
	band				
Trace	hand				
	end				
Cover	lend				
	send				
Write	bend				
	from				
Check	want				

Fill the Gaps

1. (a) band   (b) want   (c) send

     ban___   wan___   sen___

     ba___ ___   wa___ ___   se___ ___

     b___ ___ ___   w___ ___ ___   s___ ___ ___

     ___ ___ ___ ___   ___ ___ ___ ___   ___ ___ ___ ___

Word Hunt

2. (a) Which word has a small insect in it?   _____

    (b) Which word can you find on a beach?   _____

    (c) Write the two smallest words.   _____ _____

    (d) Which two words start with 'b'?   _____ _____

and · end

What Am I?

3. I am part of your body.

You have two of me.

I can do lots of things.

I am a _____.

Spelling Sums

4. (a) w + ant = _____

(b) s + and = _____

(c) h + and = _____

(d) b + end = _____

(e) fr + om = _____

All Mixed Up

5. Unjumble these words.

(a) dne _____

(b) dnah _____

(c) dna _____

(d) dnes _____

Match Me

6. Circle the word in the ball that matches the given word.

(a) from

(b) band

(c) lend

from
foom
fron
danb
band
bend
lenb
lemd
lend

Unit 14

q	e	e	f	s	p	s
h	b	a	r	a	o	e
a	a	n	o	n	g	n
n	n	d	m	d	o	d
d	d	f	w	a	n	t
e	n	d	b	e	n	d
f	l	e	n	d	o	k

Word Search

7. Find these words in the word search.

and	end
sand	send
band	bend
hand	from
lend	want

Missing Letters

8. (a) ___r___m (b) l___ ___d (c) h___n___

   (d) be___ ___ (e) ___ ___nt (f) a___ ___

Missing Words

9. Complete the sentences using these words.

sand   send   from   and

   (a) She likes to eat fish _____ chips.

   (b) Can you _____ me a letter?

   (c) It is a long way _____ school to my house.

   (d) Can you feel the hot _____ on the beach with your toes?

List Words

and
sand
band
hand
end
lend
send
bend
from
want

and end

Read and Draw

10. A girl with a blue band in her hair playing in the sandpit.

[ ]

Secret Words

11. (a) Take the 'm' off 'from' and put in 'st'. _____

(b) Take the 'nt' off 'want' and put in 'sp'. _____

(c) Take the 'd' off 'send' and put in 't'. _____

(d) Take the 'h' off 'hand' and put in 'l'. _____

Spelling Patterns

12. Use the correct colour for these words.

(a) Colour all the 'and' words red.

(b) Colour all the 'end' words green.

(c) Colour all the other words blue.

bend from

band

end

want hand

Unit 15

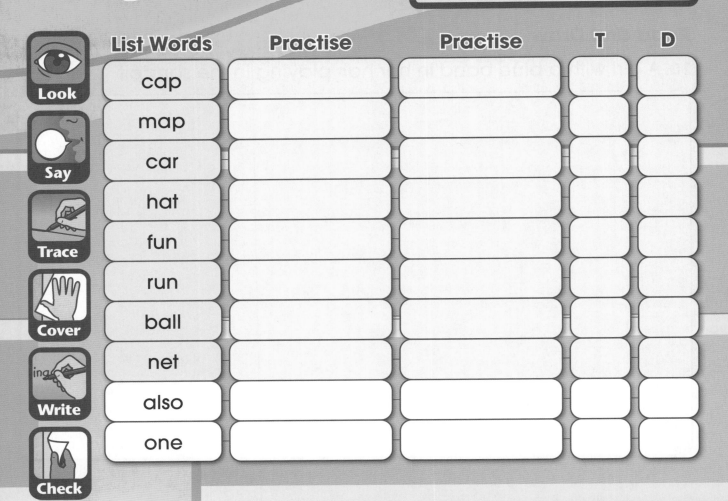

	List Words	Practise	Practise	T	D
Look	cap				
Say	map				
Trace	car				
Trace	hat				
	fun				
Cover	run				
	ball				
Write	net				
	also				
Check	one				

Rhyming Words

1. Write a summer word that rhymes with these words.

   (a) far _____

   (b) hall _____

   (c) sun _____

   (d) vet _____

   (e) rat _____

   (f) rap _____

Word Worm

2. Circle each word you can find in the word worm.

oneballalsohatcapfun

Summer Holidays

All Mixed Up

3. Unjumble these words.

(a) noe _____

(b) labl _____

(c) laso _____

(d) tne _____

Read and Draw

5. A ball going into a net.

Find the Word

6. Write each word on the grid.

Shape Sorter

4. Guess the word by its shape.

(a)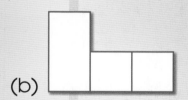

(b)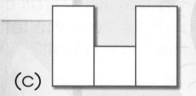

(c)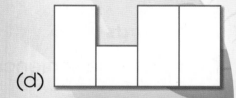

(d)

(a) (b) (c)

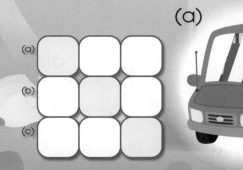

Unit (15)

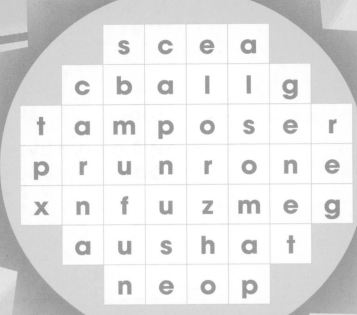

s	c	e	a		
c	b	a	l	l	g
t	a	m	p	o	s	e	r
p	r	u	n	r	o	n	e
x	n	f	u	z	m	e	g
a	u	s	h	a	t
n	e	o	p

Word Search

7. Find these words in the sunshine word search.

cap	run
map	ball
car	net
hat	also
fun	one

Word Maker

8. How many list words can you make from the letters on the beach ball?

_____ _____ _____

Missing Words

9. Complete the sentences using these words.

(a) Dad drives his _____ too fast.

(b) Use the _____ to find the way.

(c) Add _____ to two to get three.

(d) Put a _____ on when in the sun.

List Words

cap

map

car

hat

fun

run

ball

net

also

one

Summer Holidays

Labels

10. Label the pictures.

(a)

_____

(b)

_____

(c)

_____

(d)

1

_____

Word Hunt

11. (a) Which words end with 'un'?   _____   _____

(b) Which words have four letters?   _____   _____

(c) Which word has the small word 'at' in it?   _____

Fill the Gaps

12. (a) also   (b) run   (c) one

als___   ru___   on___

al___   r___ ___   o___

a___

___ ___

Difficult Words I Have Found

Word	Practise	Practise	Practise

My Spelling Workbook A—Prim-Ed Publishing—www.prim-ed.com

Aa

Bb

Cc

Dd

Ee

Ff

Gg

Hh

Ii

Jj

Kk

Ll

My Spelling Workbook A—Prim-Ed Publishing—www.prim-ed.com

Mm

Nn

Oo

Pp

Qq

Rr

Ss

Tt

Uu

Vv

Ww

Xx

Yy

Zz

My Spelling Workbook A—Prim-Ed Publishing—www.prim-ed.com